NASA: A Quarter Century of Space Achievement

NASA: A Quarter Century of Space Achievement

Photograph: The Great Galaxy in Andromeda, Copyright 1959 by California Institute of Technology and Carnegie Institution of Washington.